SNOOPY STARS
— IN —
BROTHERLY LOVE

Charles M. Schulz

ℛ
RAVETTE BOOKS

First published by
Ravette Books Limited 1989

Printed and bound in Great Britain
for Ravette Books Limited,
3 Glenside Estate, Star Road, Partridge Green,
Horsham, West Sussex RH13 8RA
by Cox & Wyman Ltd, Reading

ISBN 1 85304 173 4

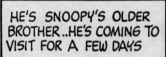

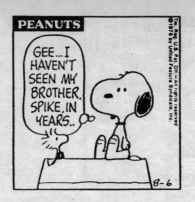

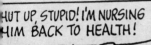

10-1

SORRY, DOG... MY MOTHER SAYS WE'D TAKE YOU HOME WITH US, BUT YOU DON'T LOOK LIKE YOU'D BE MUCH OF A WATCHDOG...

SHE'S RIGHT

WHILE I WAS TALKING TO HER, SOMEONE STOLE MY SIGN!

PEANUTS

Dear Roundheaded Kid, I still haven't found Belle.

I am writing this letter in a store that sells typewriters.

Right now, a clerk is eyeing me rather suspiciously.

WHAT'S THE MATTER? DON'T I LOOK LIKE A CUSTOMER?

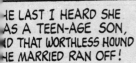

6-29

© 1978 United Feature Syndicate, Inc.

I HEAR YOUR BROTHER SPIKE IS COMING TO VISIT

NOT TO VISIT, TO **STAY**! THE COYOTES KICKED HIM OUT... HE HATES TO LEAVE NEEDLES...

ALTHOUGH, HE HASN'T FELT WELL LATELY... HE'S LOST WEIGHT AGAIN, AND HE'S BEEN DEPRESSED...

7-17

I KNOW THAT FEELING... I'M ALWAYS AFRAID I'M GOING TO OUTLIVE MY TEETH!

SCHULZ

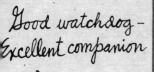

GOOD MORNING! I'M TRYING TO FIND A HOME FOR THIS BEAUTIFUL DOG

WHAT'S HIS BACKGROUND?

© 1978 United Feature Syndicate, Inc.

HE'S BEEN LIVING JUST OUTSIDE NEEDLES WITH A BUNCH OF COYOTES

7-24

I THINK I'D RATHER HAVE ONE OF THE COYOTES!

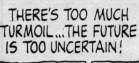

HEY, CHUCK! THAT WEIRD DOG OF YOURS IS SORT OF A BEAGLE, ISN'T HE?

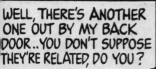

WELL, THERE'S ANOTHER ONE OUT BY MY BACK DOOR.. YOU DON'T SUPPOSE THEY'RE RELATED, DO YOU?

9-27

THAT MUST BE "MARBLES"! HE'S ANOTHER ONE OF SNOOPY'S BROTHERS! WE'VE BEEN EXPECTING HIM!!

STAY THERE, MUTT! I'VE FOUND WHERE YOU BELONG!

"MUTT"?

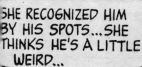

I GUESS I'VE LIVED WITH FOUR OR FIVE DIFFERENT FAMILIES...I'M NOT SURE...

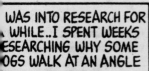

WAS INTO RESEARCH FOR A WHILE..I SPENT WEEKS ESEARCHING WHY SOME OGS WALK AT AN ANGLE

I DECIDED IT'S TO KEEP THEIR BACK FEET FROM HITTING THEIR FRONT FEET

10-1

THAT'S PRETTY DEEP STUFF..

SOMEONE HAD TO DO IT!

© 1982 United Feature Syndicate, Inc.

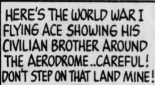

YOUR BROTHER LEFT TOWN HIS MORNING

MARBLES IS GONE?

I HAVE THE FEELING HE NEVER QUITE UNDERSTOOD THAT WHOLE RED BARON SOPWITH CAMEL THING...

ANYWAY, IT'S ALMOST SUPPERTIME..WHERE DO YOU WANT TO EAT TONIGHT?

10-11

RIGHT HERE AT THE OFFICER'S CLUB

© 1982 United Feature Syndicate Inc.

HEY, CHUCK..I JUST SAW SNOOPY'S BROTHER GOING PAST OUR HOUSE.. I THOUGHT HE WAS LIVING WITH YOU...

I GUESS IT DIDN'T WORK OUT...REMEMBER WHAT MY AUNT MARIAN USED TO SAY ?

10-12

"YOU CAN CHOOSE YOUR FRIENDS, BUT YOU CAN'T CHOOSE YOUR RELATIVES"

IT'S TOO BAD..WITH MY INFLUENCE, I COULD HAVE GOT HIM A GOOD JOB IN THE INFANTRY...

SCHULZ

© 1982 United Feature Syndicate, Inc

HERE.. A LETTER FROM YOUR BROTHER SPIKE...

© 1985 United Feature Syndicate, Inc.

"DEAR SNOOPY, WELL, OUR CACTUS CLUB HAD ITS FIRST DANCE LAST NIGHT"

"ACTUALLY, THE DANCING WASN'T AS MUCH FUN AS I THOUGHT IT WOULD BE..."

OUCH! OOO! OW!! OUCH!

SCHULZ

85

Dear Snoopy,
I think I have found a new way to make some money.

8-10

Wish me luck.
your brother,
Spike

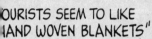

Dear Snoopy,
Our cactus club had its annual marshmallow roast last night.

I was the only member who showed up.

Which was fortunate

10-28 © 1986 United Feature Syndicate, Inc.

Because we only had one marshmallow.

Yesterday, it actually started to snow!

© 1987 United Feature Syndicate, Inc.

I was so excited I decided to build a great big snowman!

But as quickly as the snow started, it stopped.

It inspired me to write a novel.

At first, I tried writing uphill, but the words seemed to come very slowly....

3-20

Somehow, when you write downhill, the words come faster.

As you can see, however, I'm still writing longhand.

I CAME ALL THE WAY OUT HERE TO HELP YOU SELL SOUVENIRS AT THE OLYMPIC GAMES.. I CAME BECAUSE YOU'RE MY BROTHER...

NOW YOU SAY THAT A CACTUS TOLD YOU THE GAMES HAVE BEEN MOVED FROM KOREA TO NEEDLES?!

6-16

I CAN UNDERSTAND TALKING TO A CACTUS, BUT LISTENING?!

I GET LONELY..

© 1988 United Feature Syndicate, Inc.

SCHULZ

Dear Brother Snoopy,
This year I
had a great idea.

For my Christmas
tree, I decorated
a tumbleweed.

It looked really
beautiful.

12-3

But then it left!

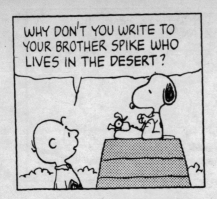

Dear Brother Snoopy,
Please tell your
friends I appreciate being
invited to the "Ugly Dog"
contest.

© 1989 United Feature Syndicate, Inc.

I do not, however,
consider myself ugly.
I am me.

1-13

Therefore, I decline
the invitation.

SCHULZ

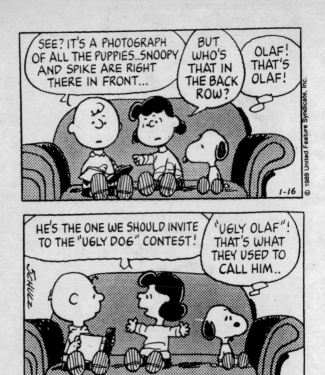

HOW DO YOU INVITE YOUR OWN BROTHER TO AN "UGLY DOG" CONTEST? I DON'T EVEN KNOW HOW TO BEGIN THE LETTER..

1-18

Dear Ugly,

© 1989 United Feature Syndicate, Inc.

May 14, 1989

Dear Mom, This is your son Olaf.

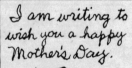

I am writing to wish you a happy Mother's Day.

Last week I was invited to go on a fox hunt.

You would have been proud of me.

I knew where the fox was hiding, but I didn't tell anyone.

Remember how you used to read to us every night?

5-14

My favorite book is still "Joe Bunny"

Anyway, Mom, have a happy Mother's Day. Greet Dad for me.

It sure is easier writing to you since you got the fax machine. Love, Olaf

Schulz

Other Snoopy titles published by Ravette Books

Snoopy Stars in this series

No. 1	Snoopy Stars as The Flying Ace	£1.95
No. 2	Snoopy Stars as The Matchmaker	£1.95
No. 3	Snoopy Stars as The Terror of the Ice	£1.95
No. 4	Snoopy Stars as The Legal Beagle	£1.95
No. 5	Snoopy Stars as The Fearless Leader	£1.95
No. 6	Snoopy Stars as Man's Best Friend	£1.95
No. 7	Snoopy Stars as The Sportsman	£1.95
No. 8	Snoopy Stars as The Scourge of The Fairways	£1.95
No. 9	Snoopy Stars as The Branch Manager	£1.95
No. 10	Snoopy Stars as The Literary Ace	£1.95
No. 11	Snoopy Stars as The Great Pretender	£1.95
No. 12	Snoopy Stars as The Dog-Dish Gourmet	£1.95
No. 13	Snoopy Stars as The Fitness Freak	£1.95
No. 14	Snoopy Stars in The Pursuit of Pleasure	£1.95
No. 15	Snoopy Stars as The Weatherman	£1.95
No. 16	Snoopy Stars as The Thinker	£1.95
No. 17	Snoopy Stars in The Mixed Doubles	£1.95

Colour landscapes

First Serve	£2.95
Be Prepared	£2.95
Stay Cool	£2.95
Shall We Dance?	£2.95
Let's Go	£2.95
Come Fly With Me	£2.95
Are Magic	£2.95
Hit The Headlines	£2.95

Weekenders

No. 1 Weekender	£4.95

Peanuts at School	£6.95

Black and white landscapes

It's a Dog's Life	£2.50
Roundup	£2.50
Freewheelin'	£2.50
Joe Cool	£2.50
Chariots For Hire	£2.50
Dogs Don't Eat Dessert	£2.50
You're on the Wrong Foot Again, Charlie Brown	£2.50
By Supper Possessed	£2.95
Talk is Cheep, Charlie Brown	£2.95

All these books are available at your local bookshop or news-agent, or can be ordered direct from the publisher. Just tick the titles you require and fill in the form below. Prices and availability subject to change without notice.

Ravette Books Limited, 3 Glenside Estate, Star Road, Partridge Green, Horsham, West Sussex RH13 8RA

Please send a cheque or postal order, and allow the following for postage and packing. UK: Pocket-books – 45p for one book, 20p for a second book and 15p for each additional book. Other titles – 50p for one book and 30p for each additional book.

Name ....

Address ....

....